Too Many Songs
by
Tom Lehrer

The subversive songs of Tom Lehrer, the mathematics teacher and sage who gave us 'Be Prepared', 'Poisoning Pigeons in the Park' and other family favourites, have corrupted millions of people and been totally ignored by millions more.

The global dissemination of his dubious threnodies over the past few decades may be blamed on his record albums and live performances and, more recently, on the stage revue, *Tomfoolery*, which was spawned in London in 1980 and has since spread to many other Lehrer-speaking countries.

This unnecessarily comprehensive collection of his songs includes the words and music (including piano accompaniments and guitar chords) of most of the songs from his three record albums, *Songs by Tom Lehrer*, *An Evening Wasted with Tom Lehrer*, and *That Was the Year That Was*, as well as three additional songs.

Too Many Songs
by
Tom Lehrer

With not enough drawings

by

Ronald Searle

Piano arrangements
by
Tom Lehrer and Frank Metis

A METHUEN HUMOUR CLASSIC

First published in Great Britain in 1981
by Eyre Methuen Ltd
Reprinted 1982
by Methuen London Ltd
11 New Fetter Lane, London EC4P 4EE

ISBN 0 413 48570 6 hardback
      0 413 48580 3 paperback

Printed in Great Britain by
Fakenham Press Limited, Fakenham, Norfolk

Contents

Foreword

The songs in this book were written between World Wars II and III, and all but three of them are from the three LPs I recorded during that memorable period in history. Most of them were intended at the time of conception either as takeoffs on various song types of the day, particularly the more sentimental species, or as commentaries on current events, so that I regarded them as fugacious ephemera which by now should have been of artifactual interest only to scholars (although in what field I can't imagine). It is therefore a source of considerable delight to me that publication of this agglomeration should be warranted at all at this late date. Any royalties will naturally be a source of even greater delight.

Three of the songs are not from my three records. Two of them, 'Silent E' and 'L-Y', were written in the early seventies for an American television series called *The Electric Company*, which was produced by the Children's Television Workshop in a desperate attempt to help young children to learn to read. An animated film accompanied each song. The third, 'I Got It From Agnes', is a recently revised version of a song I used to perform in night clubs in the fifties but did not record because it was what was called in those days a 'party song', i.e., a bit naughty. Today, of course, even though the revision made it naughtier, its innocence borders on naïveté.

The musical congeries that follows owes its existence in part to a rather curious event. An intrepid but not entirely rational young British producer named Cameron Mackintosh took it into his head that what had previously been done to every songwriter from Jacques Brel to Stephen Sondheim might be done to me, namely, a stage production embalming my old songs. The result was a revue entitled *Tomfoolery*, which opened in London in 1980 and has since been produced in various other cities throughout the world without any noticeable ill effects. All the songs used in that show are in this book, including certain alternate lyrics which I wrote for the show.

Revisiting these lighthearted and heavy-handed songs (some say it's the other way around) was somewhat like looking at one's own baby pictures: was that me? (Before I began spending so much time in California, I would have said 'Was that I?') I haven't written any songs of this type lately and probably won't be doing so, so this volume may be regarded as a definitive agglutination. (Well-wishers, however, are constantly suggesting hilarious subject matter, such as the Viet Nam war, the gradual destruction of the environment, our recent presidents, etc., so that I have often felt like a resident of Pompeii who has been asked for some humorous comments on lava.) Anyway, what good are laurels if you can't rest on them?

This is my first foreword, so please forgive me if I'm not doing it right. I believe one is supposed to thank people, but I can't think of anyone.

Except you, of course.

April 1981   Tom Lehrer

PART ONE

From Songs by Tom Lehrer

The Irish Ballad

Words and Music by Tom Lehrer

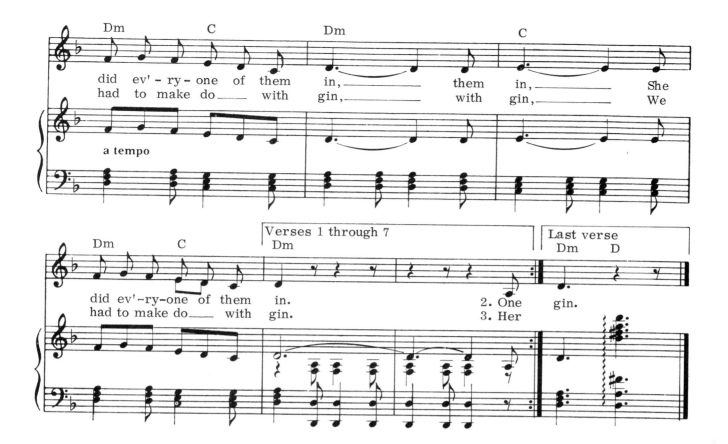

did ev'-ry-one of them in, ____ them in, ____ She
had to make do ____ with gin, ____ with gin, ____ We

a tempo

Verses 1 through 7
Dm

Last verse
Dm   D

did ev'-ry-one of them in.
had to make do____ with gin.

2. One   gin.
3. Her

3. Her mother she could never stand,
   Sing rickety-tickety-tin,
Her mother she could never stand,
And so a cyanide soup she planned.
The mother died with the spoon in her hand,
   And her face in a hideous grin, a grin,
   Her face in a hideous grin.

4. She set her sister's hair on fire,
   Sing rickety-tickety-tin,
She set her sister's hair on fire,
And as the smoke and flame rose high'r,
Danced around the funeral pyre,
   Playing a violin, -olin,
   Playing a violin.

5. She weighted her brother down with stones,
   Sing rickety-tickety-tin,
She weighted her brother down with stones,
And sent him off to Davy Jones.
All they ever found were some bones,
   And occasional pieces of skin, of skin,
   Occasional pieces of skin.

6. One day when she had nothing to do,
   Sing rickety-tickety-tin,
One day when she had nothing to do,
She cut her baby brother in two,
And served him up as an Irish stew,
   And invited the neighbors in, -bors in,
   Invited the neighbors in.

7. And when at last the police came by,
   Sing rickety-tickety-tin,
And when at last the police came by,
Her little pranks she did not deny,
To do so, she would have had to lie,
   And lying, she knew, was a sin, a sin,
   Lying, she knew, was a sin.

8. My tragic tale I won't prolong,
   Sing rickety-tickety-tin,
My tragic tale I won't prolong,
And if you do not enjoy my song,
You've yourselves to blame if it's too long,
   You should never have let me begin, begin,
   You should never have let me begin.

Be Prepared

Words and Music by Tom Lehrer

1. Be pre - pared! _____ That's the Boy Scouts' march-ing song, Be pre-
(2. Be pre -) pared! _____ That's the Boy Scouts' sol-emn creed, Be pre-

pared! _____ As through life you march a - long. Be pre - pared to hold your
pared! _____ And be clean in word and deed. Don't so - lic - it for your

li - quor pret - ty well. _____ Don't write naugh - ty words on
sis - ter, that's not nice, _____ Un - less you get a good per -

walls if you can't spell. _____ Be pre - pared! _____ To hide that
cent - age of her price. _____ Be pre - pared! _____ And be

pack of cig - a - rettes, Don't make book _____ if you
care - ful not to do Your good deeds _____ when there's

can not cov - er bets. Keep those reef - ers hid - den where you're sure that
no - one watch - ing you. If you're look - ing for ad - ven - ture of a

13

they will not be found, And be care-ful not to smoke them when the
new and dif-f'rent kind, And you come a-cross a Girl Scout who is

scout-mas-ter's a-round, For he on-ly will in-sist that they be
si-mi-lar-ly in-clined, Don't be ner-vous, don't be flus-tered, don't be

shared. Be pre-pared!
scared. Be pre-pared!

2. Be pre-

14

Fight Fiercely, Harvard!

Words and Music by Tom Lehrer

15

have   the   will.   _____   How   we   shall   cel - e -
and   true.   _____   Come   on,   chaps,   fight   for

brate   our   vic - to - ry, ____   We   shall   in - vite   the
Har - vard's glo - rious name, ____ Won't   it   be   peach - y

whole   team   up   for   tea. ____   (How   jol - ly!)   Hurl   that
if   we   win   the   game? ____   (Oh,   good - y!)   Let's   try

sphe - roid   down   the   field, _____   and   fight,
not   to   in - jure   them, _____   but

cresc. poco a poco

16

17

The Old Dope Peddler

Words and Music by Tom Lehrer

18

gives the kids free sam-ples, be-cause he knows full well That to-day's young in-no-cent fa-ces___ will be to-mor-row's cli-en-tele. Here's a cure for all your trou-bles, here's an end to all dis-tress. It's the old dope ped-dler with his pow-dered hap-pi-ness.

ritard.

The Wild West is Where I Want To Be

Words and Music by Tom Lehrer

Westerly

A - long the trail you'll find me lop - in' Where the spa - ces are wide
(- 'Mid the) sage - brush and the cac - tus I'll watch the fel - lers

o - pen, In the land of the old A. E.
prac - tice Drop - pin' bombs through the old clean des - ert

fan-cy and the plush, Leave the snow and leave the slush, And the crowds._____ I will seek the des-ert's hush, Where the sce-ner-y is lush, How I long to see the mush-room clouds._____ 'Mid the

yuc - cas and the this - tles I'll watch the guid - ed mis - siles, While the

old F. B. I. watch - es me._____ Yes, I'll

soon make my ap - pear - ance (Soon as I can get my clearance),'Cause the

wild west is where I want to be._____

ritard. e cresc. f

I Wanna Go Back to Dixie

Words and Music by Tom Lehrer

wait-in' for the Rob-ert E. Lee. ___ (It was nev-er there on time.) I'll
ain't seen one good lynch-in' in years. ___ The

go back to the Swa-nee Where pel-lag-ra makes you scraw-ny, And the
land of the boll wee-vil, Where the laws are me-di-e-val, Is

hon-ey-suck-le clut-ters up the vine. ___ I
call-in' me to come and nev-er-more roam. ___ I wan-na

real-ly am a-fix-in' To go home and start a-mix-in' Down be-
go back to the South-land, That y'

low that Ma - son - Dix - on line. *(Spoken)* Won't - cha come with me to Al - a - bam - my, Back to the arms of my dear ol' Mam-my, Her cook - in's lous - y and her hands are clam-my, But what the hell, it's home. *(Sung)* Yes, for par - a - dise the South-land is my nom-i-nee._____ Jes' give

Slower

26

27

Lobachevsky

by Tom Lehrer

(Note: Most of the following is meant to be spoken rather than sung, freely in some cases and rhythmically in others. The specific accompaniment used by the author on his recording would require too many pages to write out and is therefore omitted. Prospective performers of the piece are advised to heed its basic precept and plagiarize the author's version.)

(The author would like to state that although Nicolai Ivanovich Lobachevsky (1793-1856) was a genuine, and indeed eminent, mathematician, the peccadillos attributed to him herein are not substantiated by history. The format of this song was suggested by a Danny Kaye—Sylvia Fine routine entitled 'Stanislavsky', and the name of the protagonist was chosen for purely prosodic reasons.)

(Spoken) Who made me the genius I am today,
The mathematician that others all quote,
Who's the professor that made me that way?
The greatest that ever got chalk on his coat.

(Sung) One man deserves the credit,
One man deserves the blame,
And Nicolai Ivanovich Lobachevsky is his name.
Hi!
Nicolai Ivanovich Lobach –

(Spoken) I am never forget the day I first meet the great Lobachevsky.
In one word he told me secret of success in mathematics:
Plagiarize!

Plagiarize,
Let no one else's work evade your eyes,
Remember why the good Lord made your eyes,
So don't shade your eyes,
But plagiarize, plagiarize, plagiarize –
Only be sure always to call it please 'research'.

(Sung) And ever since I meet this man
My life is not the same,
And Nicolai Ivanovich Lobachevsky is his name.
Hi!
Nicolai Ivanovich Lobach –

(Spoken) I am never forget the day I am given first original paper
to write.   It was on analytic and algebraic topology of
locally Euclidean metrization of infinitely differentiable
Riemannian manifold.
Bozhe moi!
This I know from nothing.
But I think of great Lobachevsky and get idea – ahah!

(Sung) I have a friend in Minsk,
Who has a friend in Pinsk,

Whose friend in Omsk
Has friend in Tomsk
With friend in Akmolinsk.
His friend in Alexandrovsk
Has friend in Petropavlovsk,
Whose friend somehow
Is solving now
The problem in Dnepropetrovsk.

And when his work is done -
Haha! - begins the fun.
From Dnepropetrovsk
To Petropavlovsk,
By way of Iliysk,
And Novorossiysk,
To Alexandrovsk to Akmolinsk
To Tomsk to Omsk
To Pinsk to Minsk
To me the news will run,
Yes, to me the news will run!

And then I write
By morning, night,
And afternoon,
And pretty soon
My name in Dnepropetrovsk is cursed,
When he finds out I publish first!

And who made me a big success
And brought me wealth and fame?
Nicolai Ivanovich Lobachevsky is his name.
Hi!
Nicolai Ivanovich Lobach -

(Spoken) I am never forget the day my first book is published.
Every chapter I stole from somewhere else.
Index I copy from old Vladivostok telephone directory.
This book was sensational!
Pravda - well, *Pravda* - *Pravda* said: (**)
It stinks.
But *Izvestia!* *Izvestia* said: (**)
It stinks.
Metro-Goldwyn-Moskva buys movie rights for six million rubles,
Changing title to 'The Eternal Triangle',
With Ingrid Bergman playing part of hypotenuse.

(Sung) And who deserves the credit?
And who deserves the blame?
Nicolai Ivanovich Lobachevsky is his name.
Hi!

(**) *At each of these two junctures one should insert some phrase in Russian (if the audience does not speak Russian) or some Russian double-talk (if it does). The author's own choices varied from performance to performance, ranging from the merely inappropriate to the distinctly obscene.*

The Hunting Song

Words and Music by Tom Lehrer

cow. I was cow. The law was ver-y firm, it

Took a-way my per - mit, The worst pun-ish-ment I ev-er en - dured.

It turned out there was a rea - son, Cows were out of sea - son, And

one of the hunt-ers was-n't in - sured. Peo-ple ask me how I

do it, And I say 'There's noth-ing to it, You just stand there look-ing cute, _And when_

some-thing moves, you shoot! And there's ten stuffed heads in my tro-phy room right

now, Two game war-dens, sev-en hunt-ers and a

pure-bred Guern-sey cow.

32

I Hold Your Hand in Mine

Words and Music by Tom Lehrer

now each time I kiss it_____ I get blood - stains on my
tie._____ I'm sor - ry now I killed you,__ for our
love was some - thing fine,_____ And till they come to
get me I shall hold your hand in mine.

poco a poco ritard.

L.H.

35

My Home Town

Words and Music by Tom Lehrer

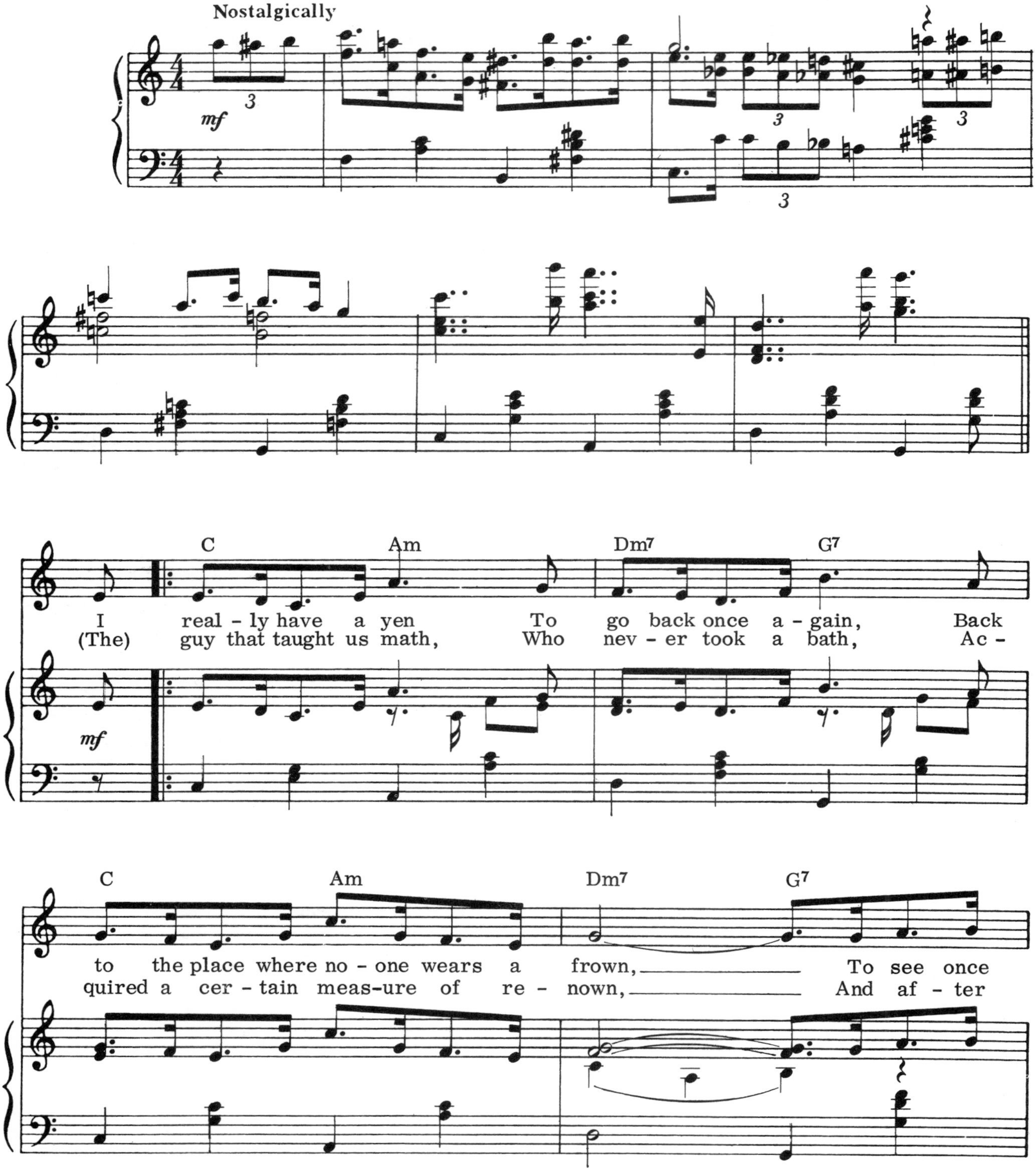

Nostalgically
mf
C Am Dm7 G7
I really have a yen To go back once again, Back
(The) guy that taught us math, Who never took a bath, Ac-
mf
C Am Dm7 G7
to the place where no-one wears a frown, To see once
quired a certain meas-ure of re-nown, And after

more those su-per-spe-cial just plain folks in my home
school he sold the most a-maz-ing pic-tures in my home

town. No fel-low could ig-nore The
town. That fel-low was no fool Who

lit-tle girl next door, She sure looked sweet in her first eve-ning
taught our Sun-day School, And nei-ther was our kind-ly Par-son

gown. Now there's a charge for what she used to give for
Brown. *(Hum)*

free in my home town. _____ I re-mem-ber
_____ in my home town. _____ I re-mem-ber

Dan, _____ the drug-gist on the cor-ner, 'e _____ was
Sam, _____ he was the vil-lage id-i-ot And

nev-er mean or or-ner-y, _____ He was swell. _____ He killed his
though it seems a pit-y, it _____ was so. _____ He loved to

moth-er-in-law and ground her up real well, And sprin-kled just a bit O-ver
burn _____ down hous-es just to watch the glow, And noth-ing could be done 'Cause he

When You Are Old and Gray

Words and Music by Tom Lehrer

The alternative version of the interlude was written for the 1980 revue Tomfoolery, in which it was sung by an older man to a younger man.

INTERLUDE

aw - ful de - bil - i - ty, A less - ened u - til - i - ty, A
joy-ing our com-pat-i - bil - i - ty, I am cog-ni-zant of its fra - gil - i - ty, And I

loss of mo - bil - i - ty Is a strong pos - si - bil - i - ty. In
question the ad-vis -a - bil - i - ty Of re - ly-ing on its du-ra - bil - i - ty. You're a-

all prob - a - bil - i - ty I'll lose my vi - ril - i - ty And
ware of my in-flex-i - bil - i - ty And my quin-tes-sen-tial vol-a - til - i - ty And the

you your fer - til - i - ty And de - sir - a - bil - i - ty, And
to-tal in-con-ceiv-a - bil - i - ty Of my show-ing gen-u-ine hu - mil - i - ty. Though your

The Wiener Schnitzel Waltz

Words and Music by Tom Lehrer

set - ting was Vi - en - nese, Your hair wore some ro - ses (or per -
par - don the sim - i - le), The mu - sic was love - ly and
teeth rath - er yel - low - ish), The mu - sic was love - ly, quite

haps they were pe - o - nies), I was blind to your ob - vi - ous
quite Ru - dolf Frim - l - y, I drank wine, you drank choc - o - late
I - vor No - vel - lo - ish.

faults, As we danced 'cross the scene to the
malts, And we both turned quite green to the

strains of the Wie - ner Schnit - zel Waltz.
strains of the Wie - ner Schnit - zel

Oh, I Waltz.

drank some cham-pagne from your shoe.

I was drunk by the time I got through. For

I did-n't know, as I raised that cup, It had tak-en two

46

bot‑tles to fill the thing up. It was I___ who stepped on your

dress___ The skirts all came off, I con‑fess.___

___ Re ‑ veal‑ing for all of the oth‑ers to see

Just what it was that en ‑ deared you to me. Oh, I re‑

PART TWO

From An Evening Wasted with Tom Lehrer

Poisoning Pigeons in the Park

Words and Music by Tom Lehrer

Spring is here, a-suh-puh-ring is here, Life is skit-tles and life is beer, I think the love-li-est time of the year is the spring. *(Spoken) I do, don't you? Course you*

50 © 1953 & 1968 Tom Lehrer. Copyright renewed

do!
But there's one thing that makes spring com - plete for me, _____

And makes ev - 'ry Sun - day a treat for me. _____

poco rit. _____

Refrain
All the world seems in tune on a spring af - ter - noon, When we're
(So if) Sun - day you're free, why don't you come with me, And we'll

a tempo

poi - son - ing pi - geons in the park. _____ Ev - 'ry Sun - day you'll
poi - son the pi - geons in the park. _____ And may - be we'll

right, When we're poi -son-ing pi-geons in the park. _____ We've
stry-ch'n-ine we

feed to a pi - geon. (It just takes a smid-gin!) To

poi - son a pi-geon in the park. _____

INTERLUDE

gained no - to - ri - e - ty And caused much an - xi - e - ty in the

The Masochism Tango

Words and Music by Tom Lehrer

dance to the Mas-o-chis-m Tan-go._____ Let our
(Your)

love be a flame, not an em-ber, Say it's me that you want to dis-
eyes cast a spell that be-witch-es, The last time I need-ed twen-ty

mem-ber,_____ Black-en my eye, set fire to my tie, As we
stitch-es_____ To sew up the gash you made with your lash, As we

dance to the Mas-o-chism Tan-go. At your com-mand be-fore you here I
danced to the Mas-o-chism Tan-go. Bash in my brain, and make me scream with

stand, My heart is in my hand,*(Spoken) Ecch! (Sung)* It's here that I must
pain, Then kick me once a - gain, And say we'll nev - er

be._____ My heart en - treats, Just hear those sav - age beats, And go put on your
part._____ I know too well I'm un - der - neath your spell, So, dar - ling, if you

cleats___ and come and tram - ple me._____ Your heart's hard as stone or ma-
smell some - thing burn - ing, it's my heart. *Excuse me! (Spoken)* Take your cig - a - rette from its *(Sung)*

hog - an - y, That's why I'm in such ex - qui - site ag - on - y. My
hold - er, And burn your i - ni - tials in my shoul - der.

soul is on fire, It's a-flame with de-sire. Which is
Frac-ture my spine, And swear that you're mine,   As we

why I per-spire when we tan-go._____ You caught my

dance to the Mas-o - -chis-m Tan-go.

INTERLUDE (somewhat slower)

nose_____ in your left cas-ta - net, love,_____ I can feel the pain
                                                  (Alternate:) I can nev-er for -

yet, love,_____ Ev-'ry time I hear drums._____
get, *love,*_____ *How this pas-sion was born.*_____

And I en-vy the rose_____ That you held in your
*How I en-vied the rose*_____ *That your teeth used to*

teeth, love,_____ With the thorns un-der-neath, love,_____
clench, *love,*_____ *When I tried some-thing French, love,*_____

_____ Stick-ing in-to your gums. Your
_____ *All I got was a thorn.*

A Christmas Carol

Words and Music by Tom Lehrer

60

E - ven though the pros-pect sick-ens, Broth-er, here we go a - gain. On
Sen - ti - ment will not en-dear it, What's im-por-tant

Christ-mas Day you can't get sore, Your fel - low man you must a-dore, There's

time to rob him all the more The oth-er three hun-dred and six - ty four. Re-

poco a poco ritard.

is the price. Hark, the *Her -ald Trib - une* sings, Ad-ver-tis - ing won-drous things. God

61

Faster

rest you mer-ry merchants, may you make the Yuletide pay. **Slower** An-gels we have

heard on high Tell us to go out and buy! So **Tempo I** let the rau-cous

sleigh-bells jin-gle, Hail our dear old friend Kriss Kringle, Driv-ing his rein-deer a-

cross the sky. Don't stand underneath when they fly by.

The Elements

Words by Tom Lehrer
Music by Sir Arthur Sullivan

te‑ti‑um, va‑na‑di‑um, And lan‑tha‑num and os‑mi‑um and as‑ta‑tine and ra‑di‑um, And
plat‑i‑num, plu‑to‑ni‑um, Pal‑la‑di‑um, pro‑me‑thi‑um, po‑tas‑si‑um, po‑lo‑ni‑um, And

gold and pro‑tac‑ti‑ni‑um and in‑di‑um and gal‑li‑um, And i‑o‑dine and tho‑ri‑um and
tan‑ta‑lum, tech‑ne‑ti‑um, ti‑ta‑ni‑um, tel‑lu‑ri‑um, And cad‑mi‑um and cal‑ci‑um and

a tempo

thu‑li‑um and thal‑li‑um. There's
chro‑mi‑um and cu‑ri‑um. There's

yt‑tri‑um, yt‑ter‑bi‑um, ac‑tin‑i‑um, ru‑bid‑i‑um, And bo‑ron, ga‑do‑lin‑i‑um, ni‑
sul‑fur, cal‑i‑for‑ni‑um, and fer‑mi‑um, ber‑ke‑li‑um, And al‑so men‑de‑le‑vi‑um, ein‑

o-bi-um, i-rid-i-um, And stron-ti-um and sil-i-con and silver and sa-ma-ri-um, And
stei-ni-um, no-be-li-um, And ar-gon, kryp-ton, ne-on, ra-don, xe-non, zinc and rho-di-um, And

bis-muth, bro-mine, lith-i-um, be-ryl-li-um, and ba-ri-um.
chlo-rine, car-bon, co-balt, cop-per, tung-sten, tin and so-di-um.

These are the only ones of which the news has come to Ha'vard, And there

poco a poco ritard.

may be man-y oth-ers, but they have-n't been dis-ca-vard.

a tempo

Bright College Days

Words and Music by Tom Lehrer

I - vy cov-ered pro - fes - sors in i - vy cov - ered halls.
We shall ne'er for - get thee, thou gol -den col - lege days.

Turn on the spig -ot, Pour the beer and swig it, And

gau -de - a - mus ig - it - ur. Hearts full of youth,

somewhat faster

Hearts full of truth, Six parts gin to one____ part ver-mouth!

sfz

She's My Girl

Words and Music by Tom Lehrer

Torchily

Sharks got-ta swim, and bats got-ta fly, I got-ta love one

wom-an till I die. To Ed or Dick or Bob She

may be just a slob, But to me, She's my girl. In

69

love her.___ The girl that I la-ment for, The girl my mon-ey's spent for, The

girl my back is bent for, The girl I owe the rent for, The

girl I gave up Lent for Is the girl that heav-en meant for

me.___ So though for break-fast she makes cof-fee that

71

In Old Mexico

Words and Music by Tom Lehrer

When it's fi - es - ta time in Gua-da - la - ja - ra, Then I long to be back once a - gain In old Mex - i - co. Where we lived for to-day, nev-er

72

giv – ing a thought to to – ma – ra_____ To the strum-ming of gui –

tars In a hun-dred grub-by bars I would whis-per 'Te a - mo'._____

_____ The ma – ri – ach – is would ser – e – nade And they

would not shut up till they were paid. We ate, we drank, and we were

merry, And we got ty-phoid and dys-en-ter-y. But

Freely, with motion

best of all, we went to the Pla-za de Tor-os, Now when-

ev-er I start feel-ing mo-rose, I re-vive by re-call-ing that

scene. And names_____ like Bel-

74

mon-te, Do-min-guín, and Ma-no – le - te,   If I live to a hun-dred and

eight – e,   I shall nev – er for-get what they mean.

Moderately

Fairly fast

(Spoken) For there is surely nothing more beautiful in this world than the sight of a lone man facing
singlehandedly a half a ton of angry pot roast!

Out came the mat-a-dor who must have been pot-ted or slight-ly in-sane, but who looked rath-er bored. Then the pic-a-dors of course, Each one on his horse. I shout-ed 'O - lé' ev-'ry time one was gored.

I cheered at the ban-de-ril-ler-os' dis-play, As they stuck the bull in their own clev-er way, For I had-n't had so much fun since the day My broth-er's dog Ro - ver got run o - ver.

poco rit. *mf* a tempo

a tempo

(last time)

(Spoken) *Rover was killed by a Pontiac. And it was done with such grace and artistry that the witnesses awarded the driver both ears and tail -- but I digress.* The

f (repeat as necessary)

mo - ment had come, I swal - lowed my gum, We
crowd held its breath, Hop - ing that death would

mf

knew there'd be blood on the sand pret - ty soon.
bright - en an oth - er - wise dull af - ter - noon.

f

The At last, the mat - a - dor

poco rit. a tempo

mf

did what we want-ed him to, He raised his sword and his aim was true, In that mo-ment of truth I sud-den-ly knew That some-one had sto-len my wal-let.

Now it's fi-es-ta time in Ak-ron, O-hi-o,

But it's back to old Gua-da-la - ja-ra I'm longing to go. ____

Far a - way from the strikes of the A. F. of L. and C. I. O. ____
(Alternate:) For though try, as I may, I can nev - er re-pay all that I owe ____

How I wish I could get back to the land of the wet-back and for-get the Al - a -
To the land of ma - ña - na And cheap ma-ri - jua-na (It's so ea - sy to

mo, ____ In old Mex-i - co. ____ *(Spoken) O - lé!*
grow) ____

cresc. poco a poco

f

We Will All Go Together
When We Go

Words and Music by Tom Lehrer

When you at-tend a fu-ne-ral, It is sad to think that soon-er o' la-ter those you love will do the same for you. And you may have thought it tra-gic, Not to men-tion oth-er ad-jec-tives, to think of all the weep-ing they will

do (but don't you worry.) No more ashes, no more sack- And an armband made of black cloth will
cloth

some-day never more a-dorn a sleeve.   For if the bomb that drops on you gets your

friends and neigh-bors too,   There'll be   no - bod-y   left be-hind   to   grieve.

poco più mosso

Chorus   **Moderately bright (in 2)**

1. And   we   will   all   go   to-geth-er   when   we   go, ____
(2. And   we   will)   all   bake   to-geth-er   when   we   bake, ____

fused with an in-can-des-cent glow._____ No-one will
let there be no moan-ing of the bar._____ Just sing

have the en-du-rance to col-lect on his in-su-rance, Lloyd's of
out a Te De-um when you see that I. C. B. M., And the

Lon-don will be load-ed when they go._____ We will
par-ty will be come-as-you-are._____ We will

all fry to-geth-er when we fry._____ We'll be
all burn to-geth-er when we burn._____ There'll be

storm_____ be - fore_____ the calm._____ 2. And we will

journ._____ You will all go di-rect-ly to your re-spec-tive Val-

hal - las.___ Go di - rect-ly, do not pass Go, do not col-lect two hun-dred

dol - las.___ And we will all go to - geth - er when we

PART THREE

From **That Was the Year That Was** etc.

National Brotherhood Week

Words and Music by Tom Lehrer

1. Oh, the white folks hate the black folks, And the black folks hate the white folks. To hate all but the right folks is an old es-tab-lished rule. But dur-ing Na-tion-al Broth-er-hood Week, Na-tion-al

2. (Oh, the) poor folks hate the rich folks, And the rich folks hate the poor folks. All of my folks hate all of your folks, it's A-mer-ican as ap-ple pie. But dur-ing Na-tion-al Broth-er-hood Week, Na-tion-al

3. (Oh, the) Prot-es-tants hate the Cath-o-lics, And the Cath-o-lics hate the Prot-es-tants, And the Hin-dus hate the Mos-lems, and ev'ry-bo-dy hates the Jews. But dur-ing Na-tion-al Broth-er-hood Week, Na-tion-al

90

Broth-er-hood Week, It's Na - tion-al Ev'-ry-one-smile-at - one - an - oth-er-hood Week, Be nice to peo - ple who are in - fe - ri - or to you. It's on-ly for a week, so have no fear,_____ Be grate - ful that it does-n't last all year._____

poco a poco cresc.

ff

sfz

92

MLF Lullaby

Wiegenliedig

Words and Music by Tom Lehrer

Sleep, ba-by, sleep, in peace may you slum-ber, No dan-ger lurks, your
Why should-n't they have nu-cle-ar war-heads? Eng-land says no, but

sleep to en-cum-ber, We've got the mis-siles, peace to de-ter-mine, And
they all are sore-heads, I say a by-gone should be a by-gone,

one of the fin-gers on the but-ton will be Ger-man.
Let's make peace the way we did in Stan-ley-ville and Sai-gon.

Once all the Ger-mans were war-like and mean, But that could-n't hap-pen a-

gain. We taught them a les-son in nine-teen eight-een, And

they've hard-ly both-ered us since then. So sleep well, my dar-ling, the
(Alternate:) So *sleep, ba-by, sleep, your*

poco rit.   a tempo

sand – man can lin – ger, We know our bud – dies won't give us the fin – ger,
eyes should be shut – tin', We know our bud – dies won't fool with the but – ton,

Heil, hail the Wehr – macht, I mean the Bun – des – wehr, Hail to our loy – al al –

ly! M. L. F. will scare Brezh – nev, I

hope he is half as scared as I.

The Folk Song Army

Words and Music by Tom Lehrer

Strum your frus-tra-tions a - way, Some peo-ple may pre-fer ac - tion, But give me a folk song an - y old day. The tune don't have to be clev - er, And it don't matter if you put a cou-pla ex-tra syl - la-bles in - to a line. It sounds more eth - nic if it

ain't good Eng - lish, and it don't e - ven got-ta rhyme. *Excuse me - rhyne!* Re -

(Sung)
(Spoken)

mem - ber the war a - gainst Fran - co? That's the

kind where each of us be - longs, Though

he may have won all the bat - tles, We had

all the good songs._____ So join in the Folk Song Ar – my, Gui – tars are the weap-ons we bring to the fight a-gainst pov – er-ty, war, and in-jus-tice, Read-y!__ Aim! Sing!_____

99

Smut

Words and Music by Tom Lehrer

ray! (Spoken) *Let's hear it for the Supreme Court!* Don't let them take it

(Sung)

poco a poco cresc.

a - way!

Interlude

(Spoken) *Bring on the obscene movies, murals, postcards, neckties, samplers, stained-glass windows, tattoos, anything!* More, more, I'm

mp

poco a poco cresc.

still not satisfied! (Sung) Sto - ries of tor - tures, used by de -

bauch - ers, lu - rid, li - cen - tious and vile, Make me

smile. Nov - els that pan - der to

my taste for can - dor give me a pleas-ure__ sub-lime.__ (Spoken) Let's

face it, I love slime. (Sung) All books can be in - de-cent books though re-cent books are bold - er, For filth (I'm glad to say) is in the mind of the be-hold - er; When cor-rect-ly viewed, Ev -'ry-thing is lewd. *(Spoken) I could tell you things a-bout Pe-ter Pan, And the Wiz-ard of Oz, there's a dir-ty old man!* I (Sung)

D.S. al Fine 𝄋

tacet

Send the Marines

Words and Music by Tom Lehrer

alla collo di pelle

When some-one makes a move of which we don't ap-prove,
(We'll) send them all we've got, John Wayne and Ran-dolph Scott,
Who is it that Re-mem-ber those ex-

al-ways in-ter-venes?_____ U. N. and O. A. S., they have their place, I
cit-ing fight-ing scenes?_____ To the shores of Trip-o-li, but not to Mis-sis-

guess, But first send the Ma-rines! We'll What do we do?
sip-po-li,

We send the Ma-rines! For might makes right, And

till they've seen the light, They've got to be pro-tect-ed, All their rights re-

spect-ed, Till some-bod-y we like can be e-lect-ed. Mem-bers of the

corps all hate the thought of war, They'd rath-er kill them off by peace-ful means. Stop call-ing it ag-gres-sion, we hate that ex-pres-sion, We on-ly want the world to know that we sup-port the sta-tus quo. They love us ev-'ry-where we go, So when in doubt,_____ send the Ma-rines!_____

108

New Math

Words and Music by Tom Lehrer

(Note: Except for the refrain there is no melody to this song. The words are to be spoken rhythmically to an underlying 2/4 beat, except for the words in italics, which are spoken freely. The specific accompaniment used by the author on his recording would require too many pages to write out and is therefore omitted.)

$$\begin{array}{r} 342 \\ -173 \\ \hline 169 \end{array}$$

You can't take three from two,
Two is less than three,
So you look at the four in the tens place.
Now that's really four tens,
So you make it three tens,
Regroup, and you change a ten to ten ones,
And you add them to the two and get twelve,
And you take away three, that's nine.
Is that clear?

Now instead of four in the tens place
You've got three,
'Cause you added one,
That is to say, ten, to the two,
But you can't take seven from three,
So you look in the hundreds place.

From the three you then use one
To make ten tens...
(And you know why four plus minus one
Plus ten is fourteen minus one?
'Cause addition is commutative, right!)...
And so you've got thirteen tens,
And you take away seven,
And that leaves five...

Well, six actually,
But the idea is the important thing!

Now go back to the hundreds place,
And you're left with two,
And you take away one from two,
And that leaves...?

Everybody get one?
Not bad for the first day!

(Sing refrain)

REFRAIN

Hoo-ray for new math, New-hoo-hoo math,＿ It

won't do you a bit of good＿ to re - view math.＿ It's so

sim - ple, so ver - y sim - ple, that

on - ly a child can do it!

Now, actually, that is not the answer that I had in mind, because the book that I got this problem out of wants you to do it in base eight. But don't panic. Base eight is just like base ten really – if you're missing two fingers. Shall we have a go at it?

$$342_{eight}$$
$$-173_{eight}$$
$$147_{eight}$$

You can't take three from two,
Two is less than three,
So you look at the four in the eights place.
Now that's really four eights,
So you make it three eights,
Regroup, and you change an eight to eight ones,
And you add them to the two,
And you get one-two base eight,
Which is ten base ten,
And you take away three, that's seven.

Now instead of four in the eights place
You've got three.
'Cause you added one,
That is to say, eight, to the two,
But you can't take seven from three,
So you look at the sixty-fours.

Sixty-four? "How did sixty-four get into it?"
I hear you cry. Well, sixty-four is eight squared,
don't you see? (Well, you ask a silly question,
and you get a silly answer.)

From the three you then use one
To make eight eights,
And you add those eights to the three,
And you get one-three base eight,
Or, in other words,
In base ten you have eleven,
And you take away seven,
And seven from eleven is four.
Now go back to the sixty-fours,
And you're left with two,
And you take away one from two,
And that leaves. . . ?

Now, let's not always see the same hands.
One, right!
Whoever got one can stay after class and clean the erasers.

(Sing refrain)   Hooray for new math,
New-hoo-hoo math,
It won't do you a bit of good to review math.
It's so simple,
So very simple,
That only a child can do it!

Pollution

Words and Music by Tom Lehrer

1. If you vis-it A-mer-i-can cit-y, You will find it ver-y pret-ty.

Just two things of which you must be-ware: Don't drink the wa-ter and don't breathe the air. Pol-

lu-tion, Pol-lu-tion, They got smog and sew-age and mud,

112

Turn on your tap and get hot and cold run-ning crud.

2. See the hal - i - buts and the stur - geons be - ing wiped out

by de-ter - geons. Fish gotta swim and birds got-ta fly, But they don't last long

if they try. Pol - lu - tion, Pol - lu - tion, You can use the lat - est tooth-

paste, And then rinse your mouth with in - dus - tri - al

waste.

3. Just go out for a breath of air, And
4. Lots of things there that you can drink, But

you'll be read - y for Med-i - care, The cit - y streets are real-ly
stay a - way from the kitch-en sink, *Throw out your break-fast gar-bage, and I've

2nd time: tempo ad lib.

quite a thrill, If the hoods don't get you the mo-nox-ide will. Pol - lu - tion, Pol -
got a hunch that the folks down-stream will drink it for lunch. So go to the

2nd time: a tempo

*Alternative lyrics may be used here to fit the local situation e.g.
for New York: The breakfast garbage they throw out in Troy/They drink at lunch in Perth Amboy.
for San Francisco: The breakfast garbage that you throw into the Bay /They drink at lunch in San Jose.

114

lu - tion, wear a gas mask and a veil,___ Then you___ can
cit - y___ see the cra-zy peo-ple there,___ Like lambs to___ the

breathe long___ as you don't___ in - hale.

slaugh-ter,___

They're drink - ing___ the wa - ter___ and

breath - ing   (cough.........) the air.___

So Long, Mom

(A SONG FOR WORLD WAR III)

Words and Music by Tom Lehrer

à la Cohan

So long, mom, I'm off to drop the bomb, so
So long, mom, I'm off to drop the bomb, so

don't wait up for me, _____
don't wait up for me, _____ But

But while you swel — ter down there in your shel — ter,
though I may roam, _____ I'll come back to my home, _____ Al -

You can see me_____ on your T. V.,_____ While
though it may be_____ a pile of de - bris._____ Re -

we're at-tack-ing fron-tal-ly, watch Brink-al-ly and Hun-tal-ly, de-
mem - ber, mom-my, I'm off to get a com-mie, so

scri-bing con-tra-pun-tal-ly the cit-ies we have lost. No
send me a sa-la-mi, and try to smile some-how. I'll

need for you_____ to miss a min-ute of the ag-o-niz-ing
look for you_____ when the war is o-ver, an hour and a

117

ho - lo - caust.

half from now!

Interlude

Lit - tle John - ny Jones he was a U. S. pi - lot, and no

shrink - ing vi - 'let was he.

118

He was might-y proud when World War Three was de-clared,—

He was-n't scared,— no - sir - ee!———————— And

this is what he said on his

way to Ar - ma - ged - don:

D.S. al Fine 𝄋

Who's Next?

Words and Music by Tom Lehrer

First we got the bomb and that was good, 'cause we love peace and moth-er-hood. Then Rus-sia got the bomb, but that's o - kay, 'cause the bal-ance of pow - er's main - tained that way. Who's next? Then France got the bomb but

120

don't you grieve, 'cause they're on our side (I be-lieve).___ Chi-na got the bomb but

have no fears, 'cause they can't wipe us out for at least five years. Who's   next?

Ja - pan will have its   own de-vice, Tran-sis-tor-ized at

half the price.___ South Af-ri-ca___ wants two, that's right: One for the black and one___

bomb. Who's next? Lux-em-bourg is
next to go, And (who knows?) may-be Mon-a-co.— We'll try to stay— se-
rene and calm— When Al-a-ba-ma gets the bomb. Who's next? Who's
next? Who's next?—————— Who's next?

123

Wernher von Braun

Words and Music by Tom Lehrer

1. Gath-er round while I sing you of Wern-her von Braun, A man whose al - le - giance is
2. Some have harsh words for this man of re - nown, But some think our at-ti-tude should

ruled by ex - pe - dience, Call him a Na - zi, he won't e - ven frown,
be one of grat - i-tude, Like the wid-ows and crip-ples in old Lon-don town who

"Na - zi, Shma - zi," says Wern-her von Braun. Don't say that he's hyp-o-
owe their large pen-sions to Wern-her von Braun. You too may be a big

crit-i-cal,_____ Say rath-er that he's a-po-lit-i-cal,_____ "Once the
he - ro,_____ Once you've learned to count back-wards to ze-ro,_____ "In

rock-ets are up, who cares where they come down? That's not my de-part-ment," says
Ger-man o-der Eng-lish I know how to count down, Und I'm learning Chi-nese," says

Wern-her von Braun.   Wern-her von Braun.

rall.

I Got It From Agnes

(from *Tomfoolery*)

Words and Music by Tom Lehrer

© 1953, 1980 & 1981 Tom Lehrer

Chorus

1. I   got it from Ag   —   nes,   She   got it from
2. Giles   got it from Daph — ne,   She   got it from
3. Max   got it from E   —   dith, Who gets it ev — 'ry
4. I   got it from Ag   —   nes, Or may-be it was

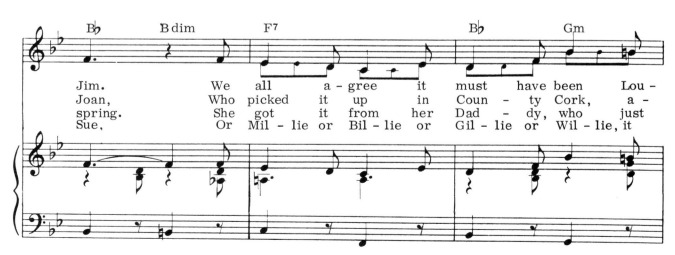

Jim.   We all a - gree it must have been Lou -
Joan,   Who picked it up in Coun - ty Cork, a -
spring.   She got it from her Dad - dy, who just
Sue,   Or Mil - lie or Bil - lie or Gil - lie or Wil - lie, it

127

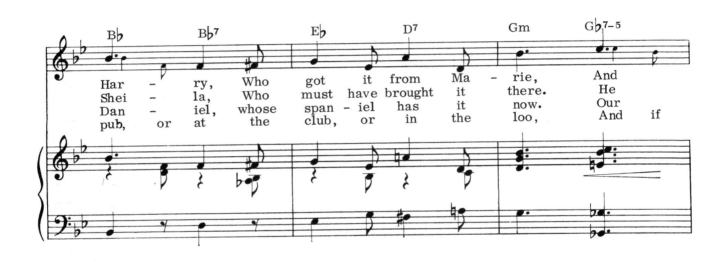

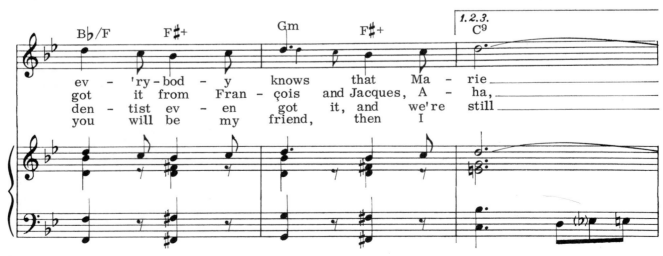

Silent E

(from *The Electric Company*)

Words and Music by Tom Lehrer

132

L-Y

(from *The Electric Company*)

Words and Music by Tom Lehrer

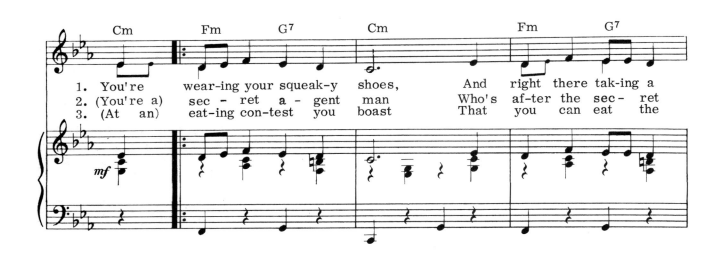

1. You're wear-ing your squeak-y shoes, And right there tak-ing a
2. (You're a) sec - ret a - gent man Who's af-ter the sec - ret
3. (At an) eat-ing con-test you boast That you can eat the

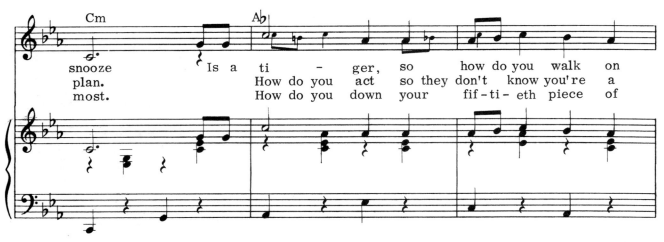

snooze Is a ti - ger, so how do you walk on
plan. How do you act so they don't know you're a
most. How do you down your fif-ti- eth piece of

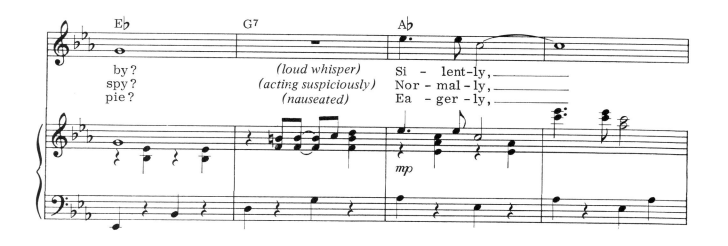

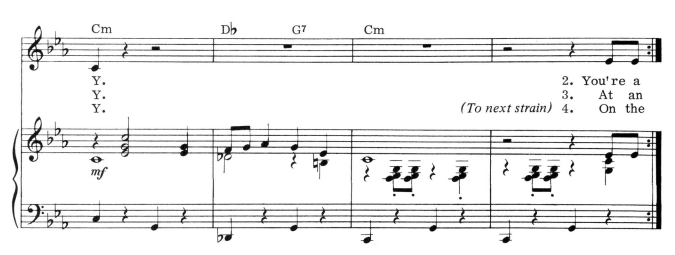

135

(4.) lake your boat up – set, And your clothes got soak – ing
5. pub – lic li – bra – ry You fall and hurt your
6. walk a – long the street A por – cu – pine you

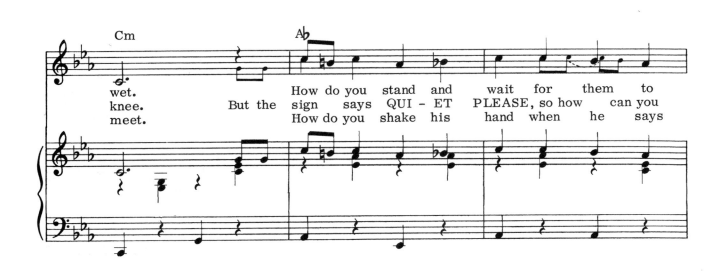

wet. How do you stand and wait for them to
knee. But the sign says QUI – ET PLEASE, so how can you
meet. How do you shake his hand when he says

dry? *(shivering)* D – d – d – d – d – d – pa – tient-ly, _____ D – d – d – d – d – d –
cry? *(crying)* Qui – et -ly, _____
"hi"? *(warily)* Care – ful -ly, _____

pa – tient-ly,_____ D–d–d–d–d–d–pa – tient – L.
qui – et-ly,_____ Qui – et – L.
care-ful-ly,_____ Care – ful – L.

Y.
Y.
Y.

(To next strain)

5. In the
6. As you
7. You

(last time ritard)

Slow and sinister (in 2)

en –ter a ver–y dark room, And sit-ting there in the

The Vatican Rag

Words and Music by Tom Lehrer

First you get__ down on your knees,__ Fid-dle with__ your ro-sa-ries,__
So get down__ up - on your knees,__ Fid-dle with__ your ro-sa-ries,__

Bow your head with great re-spect,__ and gen-u-flect, gen-u-flect, gen-u-flect!
Bow your head with great re-spect,__ and gen-u-flect, gen-u-flect, gen-u-flect!

Do what-ev - er steps you want__ if You have cleared them with the Pon-tiff,
Make a cross__ on your ab-do-men, When in Rome__ do like a Ro-man,

Ev -'ry-bod -y say his own Ky-ri- e e-le- i-son, Do-in' the Vat - i-can
A -ve Ma - ri - a, Gee, it's good to see ya, Get-tin' ec-stat - ic an'

Rag. sort-a dra-mat - ic an' do-in' the Vat - i-can

Rag!

Get in line in that pro-ces - sion-al, Step in - to that

small con-fes-sion-al, There the guy who's got re-li-gion 'll

Tell you if your sin's o-rig-i-nal. If it is___ try

play-in' it sa-fer, Drink the wine and chew the wa-fer,

Two, four, six, eight, Time to tran-sub-stan-ti-ate!

D.S. al Fine 𝄋

Discography

(All recordings are LPs unless otherwise noted)

SONGS BY TOM LEHRER
U.S.: Lehrer TL 101 (1953); Reprise RS-6216 (re-recording, 1966)
U.K.: Decca LF 1311 (1958)

Songs: Fight Fiercely, Harvard
The Old Dope Peddler
Be Prepared
The Wild West Is Where I Want to Be
I Wanna Go Back to Dixie
Lobachevsky

The Irish Ballad
The Hunting Song
My Home Town
When You Are Old and Gray
I Hold Your Hand in Mine
The Wiener Schnitzel Waltz

AN EVENING WASTED WITH TOM LEHRER
U.S.: Lehrer TL 202 (1959); Reprise RS-6199 (re-release, 1966)
U.K.: Decca LK 4332 (mono) and SKL 4097 (stereo) (1959)
(Recorded at a concert performance in Cambridge, Massachusetts. A studio recording
of the same eleven songs, without the author's spoken comments, was also released in
1959 under the title MORE OF TOM LEHRER (U.S.: Lehrer TL 102; U.K.: Decca LF 1323).)

Songs: Poisoning Pigeons in the Park
Bright College Days
A Christmas Carol
The Elements
Oedipus Rex
In Old Mexico

Clementine
It Makes a Fellow Proud to Be a Soldier
She's My Girl
The Masochism Tango
We Will All Go Together When We Go

TOM LEHRER REVISITED
U.S.: Lehrer TL 201 (1960)
U.K.: Decca LK 4375 (1960)
(A live concert version of the twelve songs from SONGS BY TOM LEHRER. The U.K.
version was recorded at a performance in Cambridge, Massachusetts; one side of the U.S.
version was taken from the same performance and the other side from some concert
performances in Australia.)

POISONING PIGEONS IN THE PARK and THE MASOCHISM TANGO, recorded by
the author with an orchestra conducted by Richard Hayman, was released as a single
record in 1960 (U.S.: Capricorn C-451; U.K.: Decca 45F-11243).

THAT WAS THE YEAR THAT WAS
U.S.: Reprise RS-6179 (1965)
U.K.: Pye R-6179 (1965)
(Recorded at the hungry i night club in San Francisco.)

Songs: National Brotherhood Week
MLF Lullaby
George Murphy
The Folk Song Army
Smut
Send the Marines
Pollution

So Long, Mom
Whatever Became of Hubert?
New Math
Alma
Who's Next?
Wernher von Braun
The Vatican Rag

SILENT E, recorded by the author with an orchestra conducted by Joe Raposo, appears
on THE ELECTRIC COMPANY (U.S.: Warner Brothers BS 2636 (1972), later re-released
as Sesame Street CTW 22052).

Note: eighteen of the songs in this book, performed by the four members of the original
London cast of the revue TOMFOOLERY, appear on the cast album of that show (U.K.:
MMT LP001 (1980)).

Index of Song Titles